THE TABLETOP LEARNING SERIES

HOLIDAYS

Special Ways To Celebrate Special Days

by Imogene Forte

Incentive Publications, Inc.
Nashville, Tennessee

Illustrated by Becky Cutler
Cover designed by Mary Hamilton and illustrated by Jan Cunningham
Edited by Susan Oglander and Mary C. Mahoney

Library of Congress Catalog Number 83-80960
ISBN 0-86530-092-5

THIS HOLIDAY BOOK BELONGS TO

Rice Grade 4
____

CONTENTS

SPRING SPLURGES

SUMMER SURPRISES

A NOTE TO KIDS

People of all ages the world over look forward to holidays as times of excitement, merriment, and joy. These are the days that bring family and friends together to celebrate who we are and where we come from, and allow us to observe in a special way the customs and beliefs that are of value to us.

This book has been written to help you enjoy the familiar holidays more, and to introduce you to some different celebrations that you may not have known about before. All of the projects, games, and activities are easy to plan and carry out, and use inexpensive materials that are apt to be found around your house.

First, look through the holiday book to select the different kinds of celebrations that you think will "fit" your family and friends. Next, mark your calendar for these days so that you will have plenty of time to make your plans and preparations.

Then you can begin to organize your project bag with art supplies, "good junk," and your own ideas for the parties, gifts, festive foods, decorations, and other special holiday happenings in this little book.

So pick your first holiday and *celebrate!*

Imogene Forte

FALL
FROLICS

MY OWN IDEAS

SCHOOL DAYS

Borrow a custom from boys and girls in Germany and make a first-day-of-school cone to fill with goodies for a younger child or a new kid in your school.

WHAT TO USE:

- colored construction paper
- pencil
- crepe paper
- scissors
- glue
- trim (stickers, buttons, gold braid, gummed stars)

WHAT TO DO:

1. Draw a curved line as shown in the diagram on the preceding page from one corner of the construction paper to the opposite corner. **2.** Cut along that line. **3.** Roll the paper together to form a cone, overlapping the two straight edges. **4.** Glue the ends together. **5.** Cut a piece of crepe paper long enough and wide enough to fit inside the cone. Glue it in place. **6.** Decorate your cone with trim and fill it with goodies.

A "ME" BOX FOR GRANDMA

The first Sunday after Labor Day has been set aside as Grandparents' Day. It is a day for showing grandparents that you care about them.

So make something really special . . .

What Grandma would like more than anything else is you! Make a "me" box so she has her own special part of you for herself.

Take a shoe box and put different things inside that relate only to you. You could write a poem, add interesting rocks, pebbles and shells you have collected, graded homework papers, samples of your artwork, homemade cookies, a book you have read and want to share, or pressed leaves and flowers. Decorate your box on the outside too, and tie it up with a big ribbon.

ALMOST-GOOD-ENOUGH-FOR-GRANDPA FUDGE

Use this simple recipe for fudge and bake some on Grandparents' Day for your grandpa. Then decorate a coffee or shortening can and put the fudge inside. It will make your grandpa smile with pride.

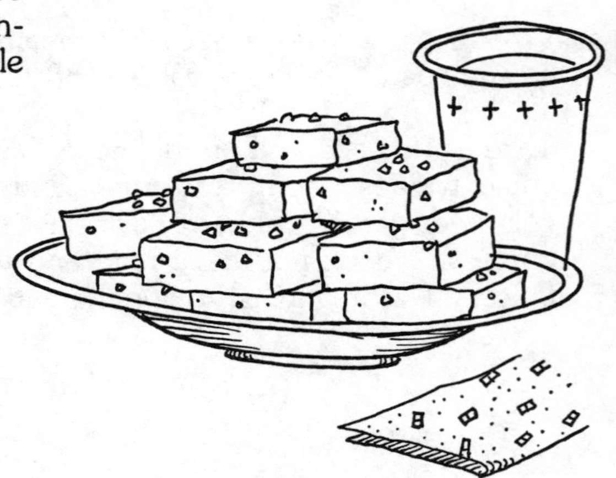

WHAT TO USE:

- 2/3 cup scalded milk
- 2 oz. unsweetened chocolate
- 2 cups sugar
- 2 tablespoons light corn syrup
- 1/8 teaspoon salt
- 1 cup cold water
- 2 tablespoons butter
- 1 teaspoon vanilla
- 1 cup chopped nuts

WHAT TO DO:

1. Scald milk (heat until tiny bubbles form along the edge). **2.** Add sugar, chocolate, corn syrup, and salt to milk. Cook slowly, stirring until the sugar dissolves. Cook to soft ball stage (test by dropping a few drops of the mixture in a cup of cold water — if mixture balls up, remove from heat). **3.** Add butter, then let cool until lukewarm without stirring. **4.** Add vanilla and beat until thick. **5.** Mix in nuts and spread in a buttered pan. When firm, cut into squares.

Wash and dry a coffee or shortening can thoroughly. Use scraps of fabric, rickrack, buttons, tissue paper, or construction paper to make a special can for the fudge. Wrap the fudge in tissue paper and put the lid on. Happy Grandparents' Day!

UNITED NATIONS DAY

The United Nations was organized by 50 charter countries on October 24, 1945, in an effort to preserve peace and form a group dedicated to international cooperation. Today, approximately 150 nations are represented, and U.N. Day is celebrated in almost every country in the world.

A fun way for you to join in the celebration is to invite your friends to a United Nations Day party. Ask each person to choose a country to represent and to bring a food or game from that country. Be sure to come to the party in traditional dress.

NATIONAL MAGIC DAY

Harry Houdini died on October 31, 1926. October 31 is now National Magic Day. It is also Halloween.

Honor Mr. Houdini by performing a little hanky-panky of your own.

All you need is a handkerchief, plenty of patience, and an admiring audience, and you'll have a "dolly dear" for a younger friend.

1. Lay the hanky out flat on a table.
2. Roll the sides to the middle.
3. Fold it in half.

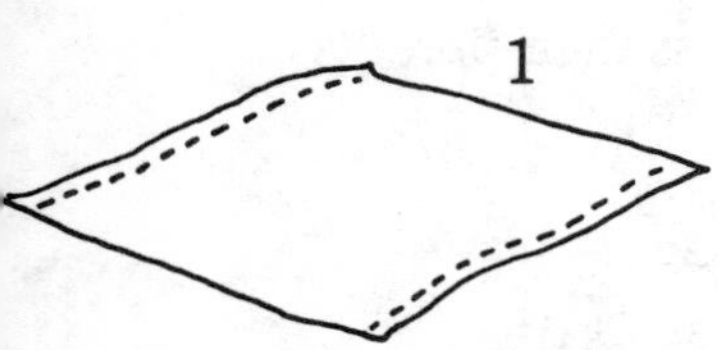

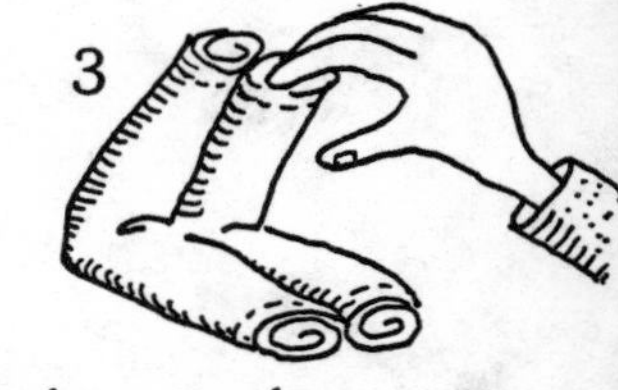

4. Pull the top rolls to the sides gently, separating them enough to tie the ends together around the "dolly dear" to make arms.

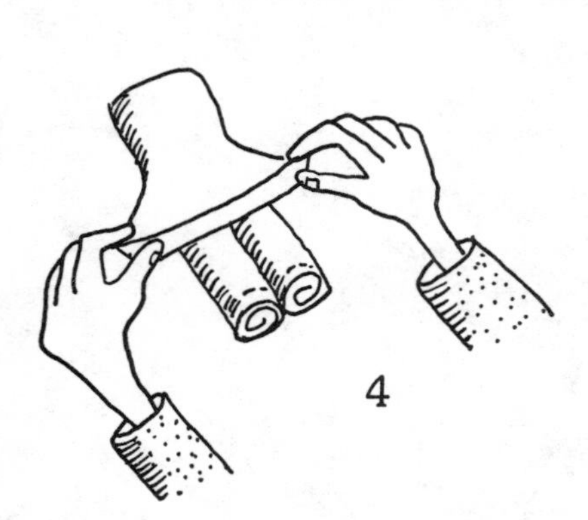

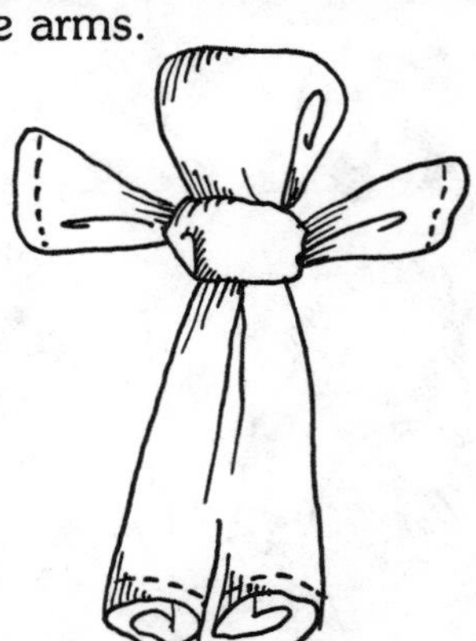

HALLOWEEN TALES

The word *Halloween* means holy or hallowed evening. It is on this evening that people of long ago told tales of seeing witches ride through the air on their broomsticks and of black cats, bats, elves, fairies, and ghosts wandering freely in the light of the full moon.

Great bonfires were built on hilltops and good luck charms and noisemakers were used to frighten away the evil spirits.

As people sat around these bonfires, they told tall tales of ghosts they had seen, witches' wings they had felt pass overhead, and of strange sights and sounds their parents had told them about.

Finish the ghost story on the following page.

We were surrounded by the thickest part of the forest. The moon was full and there was an air of mystery around us. We were walking quickly now as we made our way to the clearing we knew was ahead. Just as we rounded a corner...

A COOKIE CAKE FOR HALLOWEEN

Find a good recipe for sugar cookies. Instead of making several, spread the dough out to form one large cookie. Bake it. Decorate your creation with orange frosting, raisins for eyes, candy corn for the mouth, a nut for the nose, and pumpkin seeds for ears. Share your treat with family, friends, or trick-or-treaters.

LASTING MEMORIES

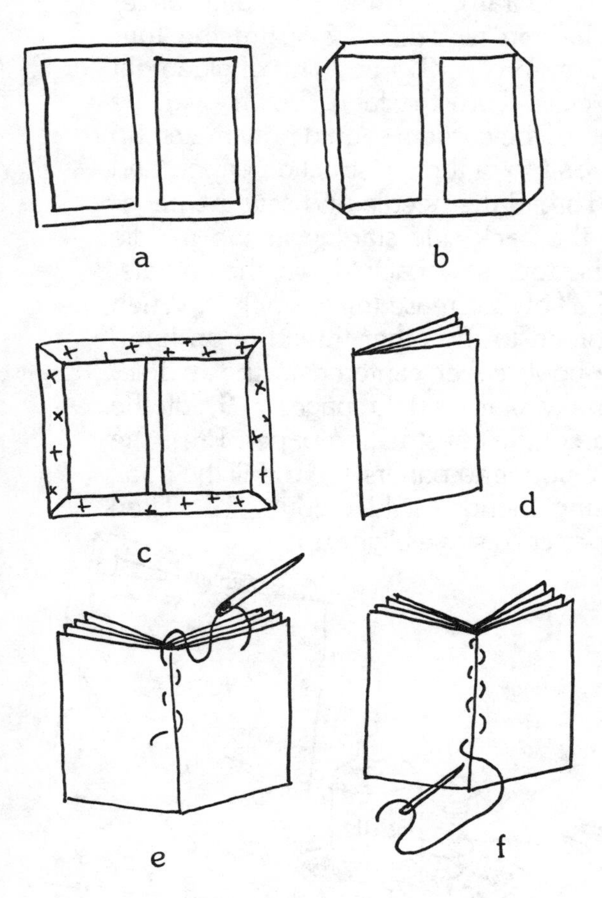

The second week of November has been declared National Children's Book Week in the United States. Celebrate Children's Book Week by making a picture book as a gift for a younger child.

WHAT TO USE:

- 2 pieces of sturdy cardboard, cut to 4½" x 6"
- cotton fabric, cut to 7" x 10½"
- scissors
- glue
- 4 or 5 pieces of typing paper, cut to 8½" x 5½"
- 1 piece of construction paper, cut to 8½" x 5½"
- white thread
- needle

WHAT TO DO:

1. Lay the fabric out on a flat surface (wrong side up) and put the two pieces of cardboard on top of the fabric(as in diagram a on the preceding page). Make sure the fabric extends about ½" on all sides. **2.** Trim the four corners at a diagonal very carefully (diagram b). **3.** Put a line of glue right on the fabric around the cardboard pieces. Turn the fabric down over the cardboard while holding it tightly in place. The corners should now match up (diagram c). **4.** Lay the typing paper on top of the construction paper, and fold them all in half (diagram d). **5.** Thread the needle and sew the pages together along the middle crease on the back side starting in the middle (diagram e). **6.** When you reach the top, sew back down the middle. Repeat the same process for the other half of the crease (diagram f). **7.** When you reach the middle again, tie the thread to the other thread in an knot. **8.** Spread the pages open inside the book cover centered in the middle. There should be about ¼" border all the way around the pages. **9.** Lift the pages up and put glue on the underside of the construction paper. Press the construction paper to the cover to make your end papers. **10.** Fill the book with pictures you think a special young friend would enjoy. **11.** Then present your gift and watch the younger child's eyes light up.

MAKE A WISH

An old legend says that the wishbone from a turkey or chicken eaten at the family table has magical power to make wishes come true. The way the legend goes, the wishbone goes to one person who selects another person to break the wishbone with. Each person makes a wish and the person who gets the bigger piece of the broken wishbone is the one whose wish will come true.

Some families allow the youngest member of the family to choose the person to break the wishbone with, others give it to the oldest, while some take turns until everyone has had a chance.

What does your family do with the wishbone?

Maybe you can think of a brand new way to wish upon a wishbone so that everyone in your family has a chance to make a wish. Try it. You might even start a tradition that will last for years and years.

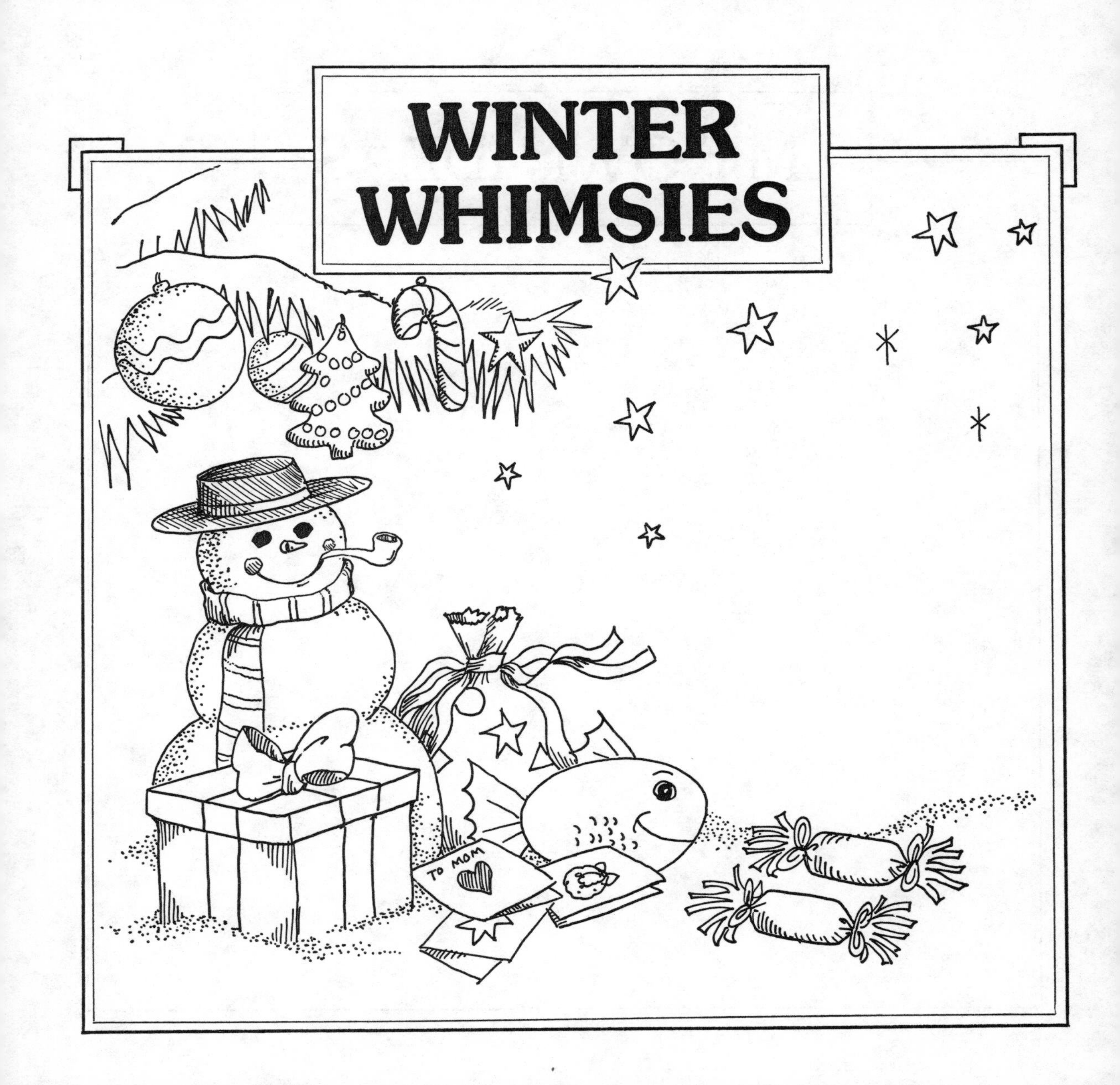
WINTER
WHIMSIES
TO MOM

MY OWN IDEAS

BUTTON UP FOR HUMAN RIGHTS DAY

December 10 has been proclaimed Human Rights Day by the United Nations.

Make buttons for people you know to wear all day to remind others of the importance of this day. Make your buttons by covering pop bottle tops with paper, writing messages on them, and gluing big safety pins to the backs.

Or, print slogans on strips of construction paper to be pasted on spring-type clothespins and then clip them on your clothes.

RIGHTLY SO . . .

Before Human Rights Day is over, ask a grown-up friend to discuss one of these statements with you. Then ask a friend your own age to discuss the same statement.

Compare the two opinions with your own to find out who thinks most nearly like you. Is it the kid or the grown-up?

1. Parents should have the right to decide what time kids have to be in bed.

2. Kids should have the right to make all school rules.

3. Parents should have the right to expect kids to have regular chores that they are responsible for every day.

4. Kids should have the right to select library books to check out without the approval of anyone else.

5. Teachers should have the right to decide how much and what kind of homework kids should have.

CHANUKAH GREETING CARDS

Chanukah, also called the Festival of Lights, is celebrated in December by Jewish families everywhere. This holiday commemorates the cleansing and rededication of the temple in Jerusalem many years ago when a cruse of oil miraculously burned for eight days rather than one.

Make some Chanukah greeting cards with potato-print Stars of David.

WHAT TO USE:

- 1 potato
- 2 shades of blue tempera paint
- small bowls or pie tins
- white paper
- knife
- pencil

WHAT TO DO:

1. Fold the white paper in half to make a card. **2.** Cut the potato in half. **3.** Draw a six-pointed star on each potato half. **4.** Use the knife to carve around the star so it becomes raised. **5.** Dip each half into the two colors of blue paint and press the stars on the paper in a design you like. **6.** Let dry, and write your Chanukah greeting inside.

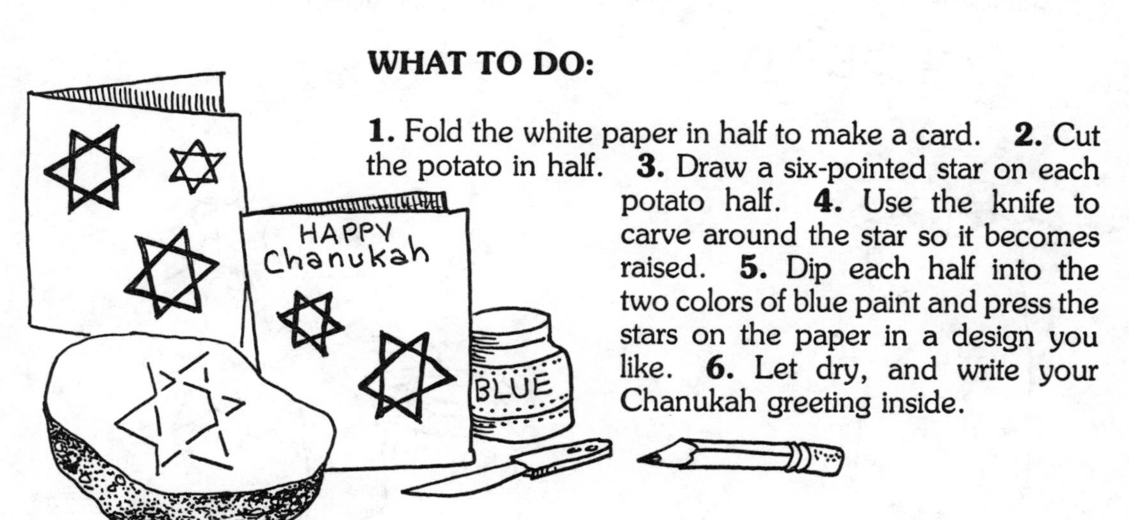

CHRISTMAS PIÑATA

In Mexico, children celebrate the holiday season by breaking a treat-filled piñata. Some piñatas are made in the shape of animals, stars, half-moons, or even people. Others are very simply made of whatever materials are available. Here is an easy piñata you can make to share with your family or friends.

WHAT TO USE:

- used tissue paper
  (save the paper from shoe boxes)
- large, sturdy brown bag
- tape or glue
- red and green paint
- paintbrush
- crepe paper
- scissors
- wrapped candies
  (or any small favors or treats)
- big stick
  (a yardstick will do)

WHAT TO DO:

1. Wad the used tissue paper into balls to make stuffing. **2.** Fill the brown bag with the stuffing and the treats. **3.** Tape or glue the bag shut. **4.** Paint the bag with the design you want. Be sure to let the paint dry before you go on to the next step. **5.** Cut the crepe paper into strips to make lots of streamers. **6.** Tape or glue the streamers to the bag to finish your design. **7.** Twist several streamers together to make a hanging loop. Tape or glue it on. **8.** Hang the piñata in a spot where there is lots of room for the treats to fall and for scrambling after them. **9.** Take turns with the stick until the piñata is broken, and enjoy the treats. Be sure to save some extra treats for the "slow scramblers."

CHRISTMAS AROUND THE WORLD

Around the world, people have found many ways to wish each other a happy Christmas.

Try to match these greetings with the countries in which you would hear them. Then practice saying the greetings until you wish your friends a happy Christmas in a language other than your own.

Feliz Navidad
God Jul
Merry Christmas
Buon Natale

United States
Mexico
Italy
Sweden

Answers: Feliz Navidad, Mexico; God Jul, Sweden; Merry Christmas, United States; Buon Natale, Italy.

HAPPY NEW YEAR TOO!

Here are different greetings from around the world that say Happy New Year. See if you can match the greetings and the countries.

Shanah Tovah
Godt Nytaar
Akemashitu Omeduto
Kwam Suk Pee Mai

Japan
Israel
Thailand
Denmark

Answers: Shanah Tovah, Israel; Godt Nytaar, Denmark; Akemashitu Omeduto, Japan; Kwam Suk Pee Mai, Thailand.

CUSTOMS FROM AFAR

These pictures show Christmas customs that are associated with Germany, England, and France.

Try to match each custom with the correct country.

Then, use felt tip pens to decorate the Christmas tree, draw a fancy plate under the Yule log cake, and place two lucky people under the mistletoe.

Answers: Germany, Christmas tree; France, Yule log cake; England, mistletoe.

SOMETHING OLD, SOMETHING NEW

Talk to the oldest person in your family about customs that your family has. Try to find out what country these customs came from, and why and how they were first celebrated in your family

Ask everyone in your family to name a Christmas custom *not* celebrated by your family, but that they think would be fun. From all the customs named, select one that can be added to this year's celebration. Old ideas are special, but don't you think it is nice to add some new ones too?

How about a roast goose instead of turkey, or would you like quail or grouse?

Maybe you could put out wooden shoes on Christmas Eve (as Dutch children do for St. Nicholas Day) instead of stockings.

Or, would you consider leaving a Reuben sandwich for Santa instead of the usual cookies and milk?

HOLIDAY WREATH

This wreath would make a fun centerpiece-and-dessert for a holiday supper. It could rest in the center of the table until the meal is over, and then guests could break off bits for dessert.

WHAT TO USE:

- 1 tablespoon butter
- 1 cup miniature marshmallows
- 1 teaspoon vanilla
- ½ teaspoon green food coloring
- 1½ cups rice or oat ring-shaped cereal
- red jelly beans
- ribbon

WHAT TO DO:

1. Using low heat and stirring constantly, melt the butter and marshmallows in a saucepan. **2.** Remove from heat and stir in vanilla and food coloring. Then fold in the cereal until it is completely coated. **3.** Spread waxed paper out and dump the cereal mixture on it. **4.** Rub a little butter on your hands so the coated cereal won't stick to them. Work quickly to shape a circular wreath before the mixture cools. **5.** Cut jelly beans in half and press into the wreath for decoration. Add a ribbon bow.

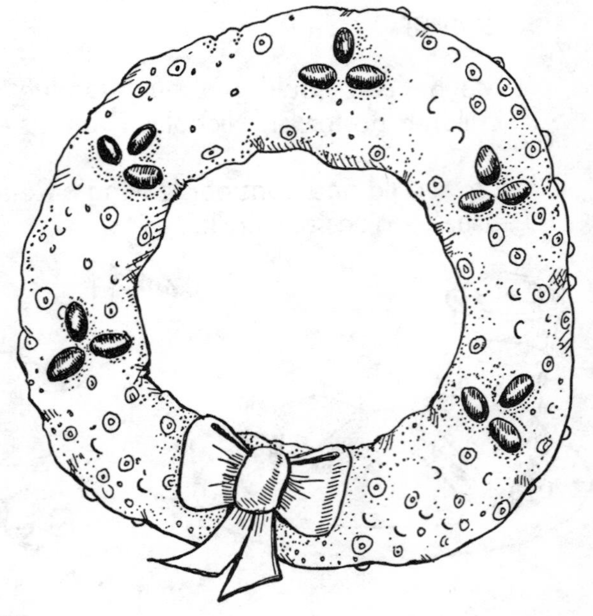

NIFTY NOTES

Say thank you in style.

Once you get into the habit, writing thank-you notes promptly and creatively becomes a fun part of the holiday season. After all, the notes always go to someone who has made a special effort to bring holiday happiness to you. Now it is your turn to send back a bit of that joy to the giver. Writing these notes helps you wrap up the holiday season until next year.

To bring extra sparkle to your notes, use dried flowers, pictures from used greeting cards, buttons, special lettering, a hand-painted design or whatever else you think will make the thank-you special.

NOISEMAKERS TO RING IN THE NEW YEAR

WHAT TO USE:

- frozen juice cans, rinsed clean and dried
- can opener
- crepe paper or tissue paper
- scissors
- ribbon or yarn
- rocks or pebbles
- wrapped candy and trinkets
- glue

WHAT TO DO:

1. Remove the sealed end of the juice can with the can opener. **2.** Wrap the can in tissue or crepe paper leaving enough on the ends to fringe. Glue in place. **3.** Fringe the ends with the scissors. **4.** Tie one end with ribbon or yarn. Before tying the other end, put a handful of pebbles, wrapped candy, and trinkets in the can. **5.** After your New Year's Eve party is over, open the noisemaker to get the goodies or take it home for a treat the next day.

CHINESE PAPER CUTOUTS

The Chinese celebrate New Year's sometime between January 20 and February 20, depending on when the second new moon appears. Dragon parades, fireworks, and paper lanterns light this special festival. Many Chinese families make paper cutouts to decorate the inside of their homes. Make some paper cutouts for yourself to celebrate the Chinese New Year. Here's how to make a fish.

WHAT TO USE:

- brightly colored crepe paper
- pencil
- scissors

WHAT TO DO:

1. Draw a fairly large oval for the body. **2.** Add two triangles for the fins. **3.** Make another triangle for the tail. **4.** Draw a heavy line around all the outer edges and cut out the fish. **5.** To finish your fish, cut scallops into the fins and tail. Cut a hole for the eye too.

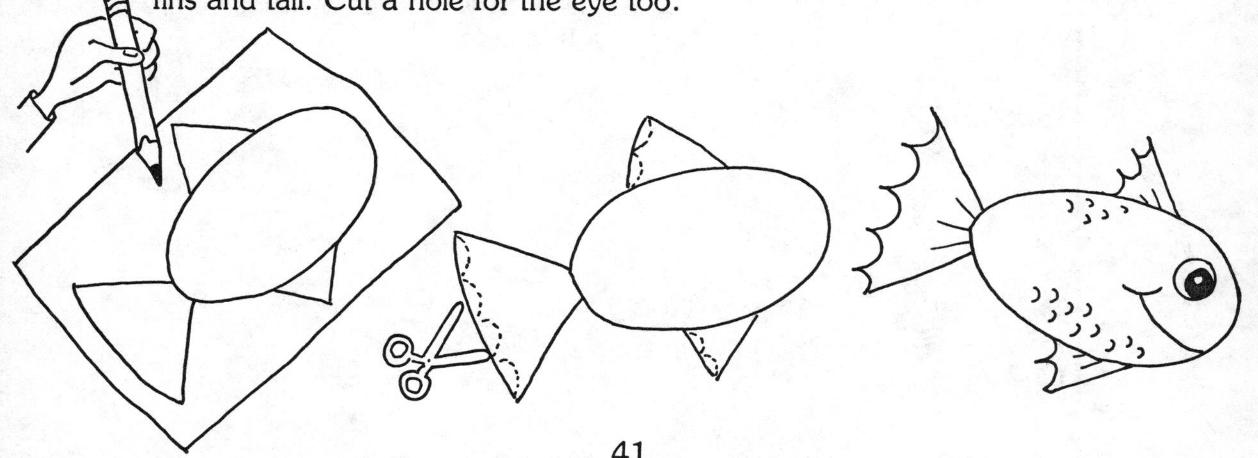

SHADOW TAG ON GROUNDHOG DAY

Groundhog Day is celebrated because of a superstition the early settlers from Germany had about planting crops. They believed that hibernating animals would come to the surface to observe the weather on this day.

If the groundhog saw the sun, his own shadow would frighten him back into his hole. That meant more cold weather would occur. If the groundhog didn't see his shadow, he would climb out of his hole and warm spring days would soon arrive.

For some outside fun in celebration of Groundhog Day — February 2 — play shadow tag. Chase a friend until you step on his/her shadow. Then turn around and run. Your friend must wait three seconds before chasing your shadow!

A LOVING CUP FOR BIRDS

Make a special Valentine's Day treat for the birds.

WHAT TO USE:

- small paper cup
- brightly colored yarn
- darning needle
- bird seed, peanut butter, crumbs, suet, small chunks of cheese, popcorn, raisins, or other edibles

WHAT TO DO:

1. Use the smallest paper cup you can find. (The waxed ones for bathroom dispensers work well.) **2.** Thread the needle with yarn. **3.** Run the yarn through one side of the cup, pull up to form a handle, then pull it through the other side of the cup. Knot the ends of the yarn. **4.** Fill the loving cup with goodies for the birds. Hungry birds aren't too particular about what they eat — lunch-box leftovers will do nicely. **5.** Hang the loving cup from a tree branch and wait for the birds to discover it.

A SPONGY VALENTINE

Now make a Valentine's Day treat for some other special friend.

WHAT TO USE:

- small kitchen sponge
- felt tip pen
- scissors
- poster paint
- small dish
- construction paper
  (folded in half to make a card)

WHAT TO DO:

1. Use a heart pattern or create one of your own to draw on the sponge with the felt tip pen. **2.** Cut out the shape. **3.** Pour the paint into the dish and dip the sponge shape into the paint. **4.** Press the shape onto the card in a design you like. You can make gift wrap paper this way too.

FAMILY FUN THE WHOLE YEAR LONG

February 24 is Gregorian Calendar Day, which celebrates the most widely used calendar today.

Make a special family celebration calendar. Find a calendar and mark all the birthdays and special days in your family (anniversaries, dog's birthday, day you get a good check-up). Mark with stickers or draw pictures on those days. Find a place in your house where everyone can use the calendar. When the year is over, you will have a decorated record to remind you of all those special times.

SPRING
SPLURGES
A
COUPON
BOOK
FOR
MOM

MY OWN IDEAS

"JUMP UP" FOR CARNIVAL

In many countries such as Trinidad, Austria, Italy, and other Roman Catholic areas, many people celebrate Carnival. It is usually celebrated the Sunday, Monday, and Tuesday before Lent with parades, pageants, feasts, and street bands where people "jump up" to the music. Prizes are awarded for the best costumes, and most stores and shops are closed.

Stage your own carnival in your neighborhood by dressing up in costume, playing homemade instruments and "jumping up" to the music.

"THE IDES OF MARCH HAVE COME"

— Julius Caesar

March 15 is the Ides of March. On this date in 44 B.C., the Roman statesman and general Julius Caesar was assassinated in the Roman senate. Caesar had been warned by a soothsayer (a fortune teller) to expect bad luck on this day.

Greet your family and friends today by saying *ave* (pronounced "ah-vay"), which is the Latin way to say hello.

To celebrate the Ides of March, dress as a Roman would. Find an old sheet that you can drape across one shoulder like a toga. Tie leaves or stems into a circle and wear it on your head like a laurel wreath.

You might want to get some friends together and have a Roman lunch. Wear togas and laurel wreaths, and feast on grapes, bread, cheese, and fruit juice.

At the end of the day, say good-bye to your friends in Latin — *vale* (pronounced "vah-lay").

ST. PATRICK'S DAY PIE

Make a green pie to celebrate St. Patrick's Day on March 17, and surprise your family!

WHAT TO USE:

- 1 small can crushed pineapple with juice
- 1 box instant pistachio pudding mix
- medium-size container frozen nondairy whipped topping
- 1 9-inch prepared graham cracker crumb crust

WHAT TO DO:

1. Place pineapple and pudding mix in a mixing bowl and mix well. **2.** Fold in whipped topping. **3.** Spoon into pie shell and put in the refrigerator for 30 minutes before serving.

AN UPSIDE-DOWN, BACKWARD, INSIDE-OUT APRIL FOOL'S DAY

Invite your family or friends to a party they won't forget. Use upside down invitations to ask your friends to think of as many ways as possible to "turn themselves around" from how they ordinarily are. Clothes turned inside out, shirts and jackets buttoned in the back, shoes on the wrong feet, and socks on heads are just a few suggestions you might give to get everyone in the mood.

Turning chairs away from the table instead of toward it, greeting people with your back turned, serving dessert before meat and vegetables, and wishing everyone good-bye when they arrive and hello when the party is over will add to the fun. Once your party gets under way, you and your guests are sure to think of your own ways to make this a party to talk about for years to come.

PINEAPPLE UPSIDE-DOWN CAKE

Serve this old-fashioned, made-from-scratch dessert to finish (or begin!) your party in style. It's a lot more fun than a cake mix and almost as easy.

WHAT TO USE:

- 2 egg yolks
- 3/4 cup sugar
- 1 small can sliced pineapple, drained (save the juice)
- 3/4 cup cake flour
- 1/8 teaspoon salt
- 1/2 teaspoon baking powder
- 1/2 teaspoon vanilla extract
- 2 egg whites, beaten until stiff
- 1/4 cup butter
- 2/3 cup brown sugar

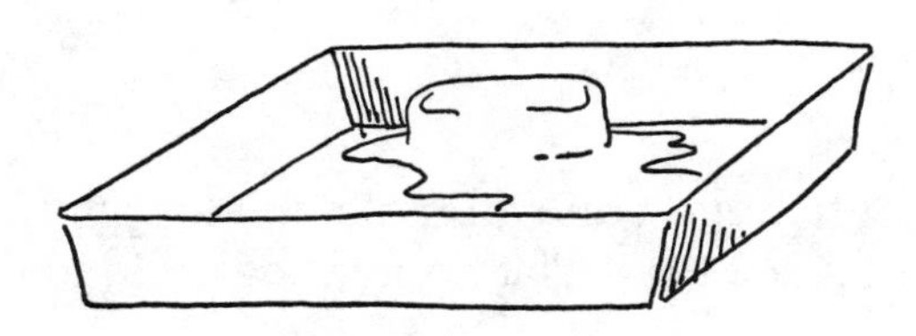

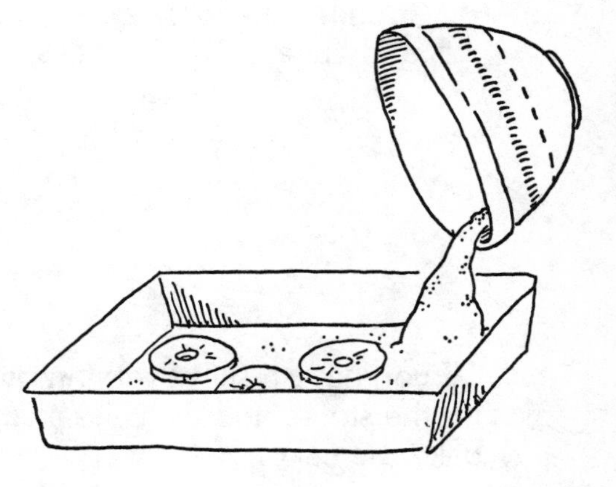

WHAT TO DO:

1. Beat egg yolks until very thick. **2.** Add sugar gradually and continue beating. **3.** Add pineapple juice and mix well. **4.** Sift together flour, salt, and baking power and add to mixture. **5.** Mix until smooth and add vanilla. **6.** Fold in egg whites.

Topping
1. Melt the butter in an 8-inch square cake pan.* **2.** Add brown sugar. **3.** Arrange pineapple slices over this mixture. **4.** Pour cake mixture over this and bake at 325 degrees for one hour. **5.** Invert on a plate to serve.

*If you have a skillet with an oven-proof handle, you can make the topping on the stove, add the cake mixture, and place the skillet right in the oven to bake the cake.

A PASSOVER RECIPE FOR YOU

Passover or Pesach is the Jewish celebration commemorating the delivery of the Jews from slavery in Egypt. The word *Passover* stems from the biblical account of the Death Angel who "passed over" the Jewish homes when the first-born Egyptian sons were killed. Jews celebrate this holiday with a special dinner called a Seder when they eat certain foods with symbolic meanings. This is a recipe for charoses, which symbolizes the mortar the Jews used to build Egyptian cities and recognizes the Jews' labor.

We're sure that once you try this, it will become a family tradition for you too.

Mix together 1 cup chopped apples, 1/4 cup chopped walnuts, 1 teaspoon honey, 1 teaspoon cinnamon, and 1 to 2 teaspoons of grape juice. You can also add raisins if you like.

SHELLS + SOIL + SEEDS = A WINDOW GARDEN

Crack your Easter eggs carefully about ¾ of the way down and peel off the top part, leaving the rest of the shell. Carefully dig out the cooked egg with a fork. Punch a small hole in the bottom of the eggshell for drainage. Fill the eggshell with soil and plant some seeds (parsley, basil, and thyme are good and grow quickly). Put the eggshells back in an egg carton and leave in a sunny window. Soon your herb garden will begin to grow. If you plant your seeds right after Easter using the shells from your Easter eggs, you should have gifts for your friends in less than a month.

To make special holders for your eggshell garden, cut out strips of pretty colored construction paper. Use crayons or paints to decorate the strips. Glue the ends together to form a ring. These would also make nice place card holders for decorated eggs on the Easter morning breakfast table.

EGGSHELL MOSAICS

A mosaic is a nice way to say Happy Easter.

WHAT TO USE:

- eggshells,
  cleaned and dried
- paper cups
- food coloring
- fork
- paper towels
- construction paper
- white glue

WHAT TO DO:

1. Crush some eggshells into small pieces. **2.** Fill paper cups about half full of egg-shells. **3.** Put in some drops of food coloring — one color
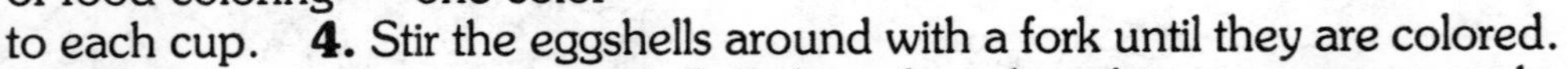
to each cup. **4.** Stir the eggshells around with a fork until they are colored. **5.** Lift them out and make little piles of each color on paper towels. **6.** Squeeze a glue design on the construction paper. **7.** Fill in the design with the colored eggshells and leave to dry.

GREEK EASTER EGG FUN

Many families in Greece play a special game at Easter — something you and your own family might like to do.

First of all, you must have enough hard-boiled eggs for your whole family. They are dyed red to symbolize joy. After the Easter morning service, each person in the family picks an egg. (Each person tries to pick a strong egg.) Then, two family members knock the tops or bottoms of their eggs together until one of the eggs breaks. The winner continues trying to break his/her egg with all the other members of the family until there is one person left with a whole egg. This person is said to have good luck for the entire year.

CELEBRATE! PLANT A TREE FOR ARBOR DAY

Arbor Day — April 22 — is a day dedicated to trees. Actually, it is celebrated on different days in different states, but the original Arbor Day was on April 22 because that is the birthday of the founder of Arbor Day, J. Sterling Morton, who started the celebration in 1872.

It's a time to think about conservation,preservation, and protection of our natural forests. What a perfect way to test your green thumb by planting a tree you really like!

You can use seeds, buy a tree from a nursery, use a seedling from another tree, or dig up one from the woods. Make sure you find out everything you need to know about your tree — how much water and light it needs, how tall it will grow, if it will bear fruit or flowers, and any other important facts that will help keep your tree healthy. Once your tree is planted, raise a toast to trees with some orange or apple juice. (Remember, oranges and apples grow on trees.)

MAY — A TIME FOR FLOWERS

For a new twist to a May Day celebration, rejoice as Hawaii does on May 1 by celebrating Lei Day. Like May Day, Lei Day is observed with flowers. In Hawaii everyone wears a lei — a garland of flowers worn around the neck.

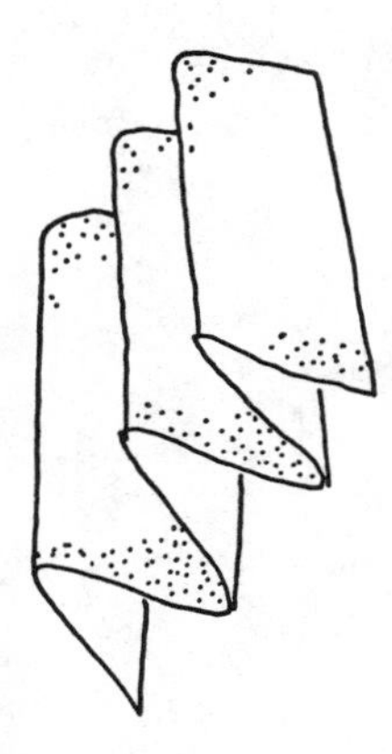

To make your own lei, make flowers as follows: **1.** Fold a facial tissue like an accordion. **2.** Wrap a bread tie around the center. **3.** Spread the petals out and tear the edges carefully to make a scalloped look. **4.** Cut a piece of heavy thread long enough to go loosely over your head. **5.** Use a needle and thread to carefully string the flower onto the lei. **6.** Make more tissue flowers as you need them. **7.** When your lei looks full, tie the two ends of the thread together.

As a variation, you can attach the flowers to pipe cleaners and make a May basket for a special friend.

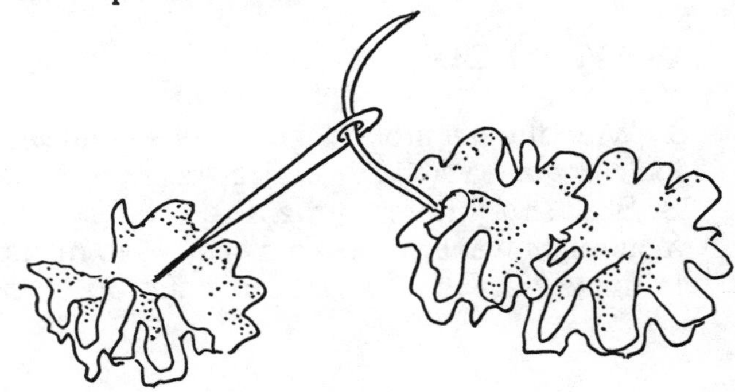

A FISHY MOTHER'S DAY PRESENT

Here's an easy, fun way to say Happy Mother's Day!

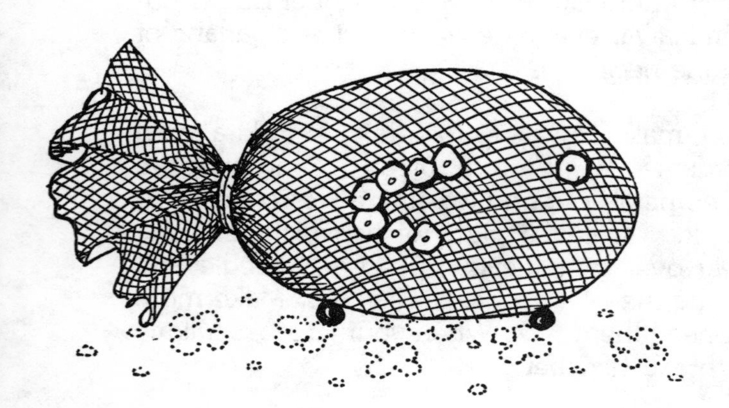

WHAT TO USE:

- an oval bar of soap
- netting
- straight pins
- sequins
- string
- 4 thumbtacks

WHAT TO DO:

1. Wrap the net around the bar of soap, leaving enough at the back to tie to look like a back fin. **2.** Tie the net at the back with a piece of string. **3.** Stick straight pins in the holes of the sequins and into the soap for eyes. You might want to use extra sequins to make side fins. **4.** Use thumbtacks to make "feet" so the fish can stand up.

A COUPON BOOK ESPECIALLY FOR MOTHER

For a very special Mother's Day treat, make a coupon book full of promises of things you will do for Mom.

WHAT TO USE:

- construction paper
- typing paper
- crayons or felt tip pens
- ribbon
- scissors

WHAT TO DO:

1. Make a cover from construction paper. Illustrate it the way you like. **2.** Punch small holes along the left side and tie it together with ribbon. **3.** Make special coupons on the typing paper that can be cut out for Mother to use. Illustrate each one. Be sure to be available when Mother decides to "cash in" her coupons!

SUMMER
SURPRISES

MY OWN IDEAS

WORLD ENVIRONMENT DAY

June 5 has been set aside as World Environment Day.

This would be a good date to plan to improve your own environment with a clean-up campaign.

Begin by checking on this list all the things that you need to clean up:

- ☐ school bag or purse
- ☐ desk
- ☐ bedroom closet
- ☐ backyard
- ☐ toy box
- ☐ dresser drawers
- ☐ other

Before you get started, get three big shopping bags and label them *give away, throw away,* and *repair.*

Sort the things as you go — you may be surprised to find a lot of neat things that you had forgotten you even owned.

CLEAN-UP LADY

Make this clean-up lady as a surprise gift to celebrate World Environment Day.

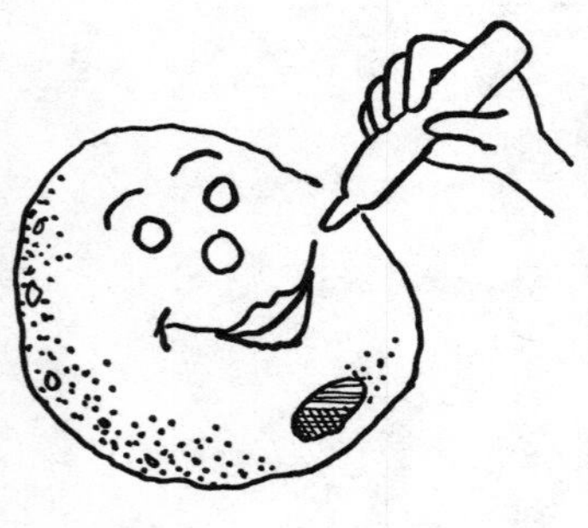

WHAT TO USE:

- an empty plastic detergent or cleaning solution bottle
- a round sponge
- 3 dishcloths
- a piece of yarn
- felt tip pens

WHAT TO DO:

1. Punch a hole in the edge of the sponge so you can poke the sponge onto the neck of the bottle to make a head. **2.** Draw a face on the sponge with the felt tip pens. **3.** Push the sponge onto the bottle. Use yarn to tie one of the dishcloths around it to form a scarf. **4.** Then drape and tie the other dishcloths around the bottle to form a dress — using one for the top half of the bottle and the other for the bottom half.

A NAME PUZZLE FOR DAD

Make a sure-to-please Father's Day gift.

WHAT TO USE:

- corrugated cardboard or stiff tagboard
- pencil
- scissors
- shoe box with top
- full-color pages from old magazines
- glue
- ribbon

WHAT TO DO:

1. Print or write your dad's name in big, chunky letters on the cardboard or tagboard. Make sure the sides of the letters touch. **2.** Cut the name out. **3.** Place the name on the inside of the top of the shoe box and trace around it. (This makes a place for the puzzle to be worked.) **4.** Look through magazines and find pictures of things that relate to your dad (things he likes to do, favorite foods, hobbies, sports, clothes, job, books, music). **5.** Cut out small pictures that will fit on the letters. **6.** Arrange the pictures collage-style and glue them on the letters. **7.** Then cut the letters apart to form a puzzle. **8.** Put the puzzle pieces inside the shoe box, tie a ribbon around it, and present it to your dad on his special day.

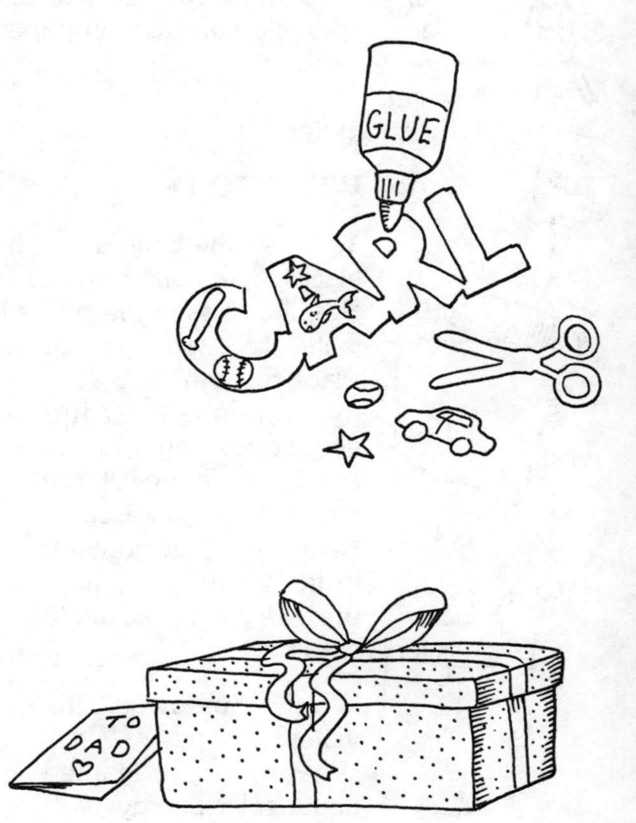

SUMMER SOLSTICE FUN

To celebrate the first day of summer — on or around June 21 — try this solar energy experiment.

WHAT TO USE:

- 3 tin cans of the same size (coffee or shortening)
- black and white construction paper
- tape or glue
- water
- thermometer

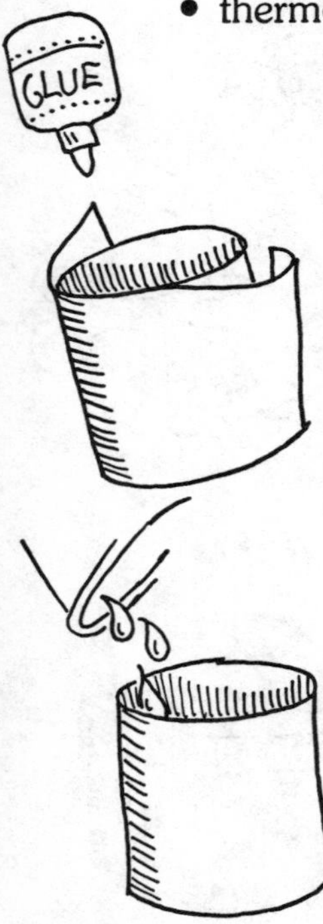

WHAT TO DO:

1. Wash the cans and remove the labels. **2.** Wrap one can in black paper, one in white paper, and leave the other can as it is. **3.** Glue or tape the paper in place. **4.** Put the same amount of water in each can. **5.** Place the can on a sunny windowsill. After about three hours, check the temperature of the water in all three cans. Keep the thermometer in the water a few minutes to get an accurate reading.

Which can heats the water the best? Why? What have you learned about solar energy?

WATER PLAY ON A HOT SUMMER DAY

The days between July 3 and August 15 are called Dog Days. That's because they are traditionally the hottest days of the year in the Northern Hemisphere. So kick off your shoes and wet down these dog day afternoons by making a water slide!

Spread a big plastic garbage bag or old shower curtain on the grass and anchor it with rocks. Lay a hose on one end and turn on the water! As the plastic becomes completely wet, you can sit down in front of the hose and slip and slide for a great ride.

INDEPENDENCE DAY – A CAUSE TO CELEBRATE

Citizens of the United States celebrate their independence on July 4 — the anniversary of the adoption of the Declaration of Independence in 1776. Festivites include speeches; family cookouts; red, white, and blue decorations; parades, and fireworks.

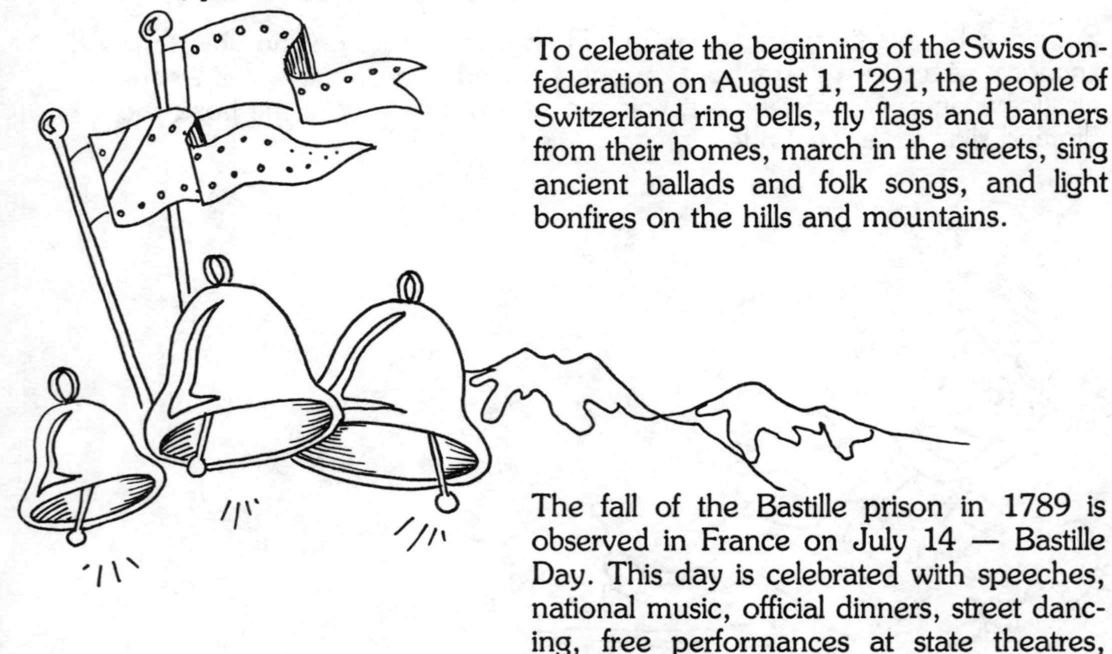

To celebrate the beginning of the Swiss Confederation on August 1, 1291, the people of Switzerland ring bells, fly flags and banners from their homes, march in the streets, sing ancient ballads and folk songs, and light bonfires on the hills and mountains.

The fall of the Bastille prison in 1789 is observed in France on July 14 — Bastille Day. This day is celebrated with speeches, national music, official dinners, street dancing, free performances at state theatres, fireworks, and the firing of a cannon one hundred times in Paris as the day begins.

Canada marks the 1867 anniversary of the confederation of Upper and Lower Canada and a few of the Maritime Provinces into the Dominion of Canada on July 1 with parades, sports events, and by singing the Canadian national anthem, "The Maple Leaf Forever."

Try to think of a special way to celebrate this special holiday. Decorate your room with streamers, cook something for the family, make independence cards to give to family and friends, or even stage your own parade.

Any way you choose, celebrate! The right to be free is worth shouting about!

Try making your own parchment paper for a scroll, then write your own declaration of what Independence Day means to you.

WHAT TO USE:

- white typing paper
- wet tea bags
- lemon juice
- cookie sheet

WHAT TO DO:

1. Dab the wet tea bags all over the paper. **2.** Squirt drops of lemon juice randomly all over the page. **3.** Place the paper on a cookie sheet and bake in the oven at the lowest setting until the paper is dry. **4.** When the paper cools, write your declaration.

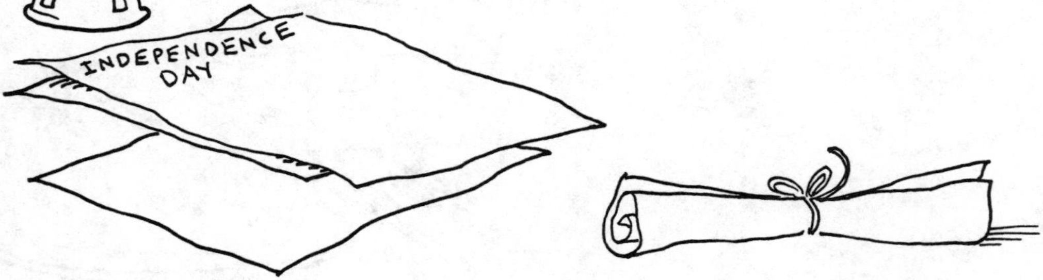

INDEPENDENCE DAY

TODAY IS YOUR DAY

Summer days get long and lazy and even a little bit boring sometimes. Holidays and special days are few and far between too. So this just may be the time to make up a holiday of your own.

Think of a good reason for celebrating . . . maybe one of these:

Apple Picking Day
Good Neighbor Day
Closet Cleaning Day
Backyard Day
Little Kids' Day
Fun-and-Games Day
Be Kind to Animals Day

TODAY IS YOUR DAY, *continued*

Celebrate your special day by selecting three to five people who live too far away to get together. Invite them to a "no show" celebration. (The number will depend on how ambitious you are.) Make up an invitation like this:

You are being invited to a "no show" party to celebrate ______ Day. This is a day that I have made up to share with my special friends. All you have to do is take the things out of this envelope and at ___ o'clock on ______ the ___ enjoy my party wherever you are.

Please wear the hat, enjoy the goodies, throw the confetti, read your note, and be happy with me!

Then make a hat, confetti, and favors; write the invitation; include gum, a lollipop, a pack of cinnamon red-hots, or anything else you have to put in a heavy envelope. Address the envelope carefully, write HAND CANCEL PLEASE on the outside near the address, add a stamp, and mail your "no show" party. Wouldn't you like to see the look on your friends' faces when they open the envelope?